I'm Glad I'm Me

POEMS ABOUT YOU

BY JACK PRELUTSKY
ILLUSTRATED BY NANCY MEYERS

SCHOLASTIC INC.

NEW YORK   TORONTO   LONDON   AUKLAND   SYDNEY
MEXICO CITY   NEW DELHI   HONG KONG   BUENOS AIRES

"I'm Glad I'm Me" Copyright © 2006 by Jack Prelutsky
Illustrations copyright © 2006 by Scholastic Inc.

Poems on pages 6, 8-9, 18 from *Rainy, Rainy Saturday* Copyright © 1980 by Jack Prelutsky*
Poem on page 15 from *It's Snowing! It's Snowing* Copyright © 1984 by Jack Prelutsky*
Poems on pages 19, 26-27 from *The New Kid on the Block* Copyright © 1984 by Jack Prelutsky*
Poem on page 31 from *My Parents Think I'm Sleeping* Copyright © 1985 by Jack Prelutsky*
Poems on pages 7, 12-14, 22-23 from *Something Big Has Been Here* Copyright © 1990 by Jack Prelutsky*
Poem on pages 16-17 from *The Dragons Are Singing Tonight* Copyright © 1993 by Jack Prelutsky*
Poems on pages 4-5, 10-11, 24-25, 28 from *A Pizza the Size of the Sun* Copyright © 1996 by Jack Prelutsky*
Poems on pages 20-21, 29-30 from *It's Raining Pigs and Noodles* Copyright © 2000 by Jack Prelutsky*

*Reprinted by permission of Greenwillow Books, an imprint of HarperCollins Publishers.

10 Book Pack ISBN 0-439-90826-4
ISBN B-OK9-90826-4

12 11 10 9 8 7 6 5 4   6 7 8 9 10 11/0

Printed in the U.S.A.
First Scholastic printing, September 2006

TABLE OF CONTENTS

When I Grow Up

When I grow up, I think that I
may pilot rockets through the sky,
grow orchards full of apple trees,
or find a way to cure disease.
Perhaps I'll run for president,
design a robot, or invent
unique computerized machines
or miniature submarines.

When I grow up, I'd like to be
the captain of a ship at sea,
an architect, a clown or cook,
the writer of a famous book.
I just might be the one to teach
a chimpanzee the art of speech . . .
but what I'll *really* be, I'll bet
I've not *begun* to think of yet.

WHISTLING

Oh, I can laugh and I can sing
and I can scream and shout,
but when I try to whistle,
the whistle won't come out.

I shape my lips the proper way,
I make them small and round,
but when I blow, just air comes out,
there is no whistling sound.

But I'll keep trying very hard
to whistle loud and clear,
and someday soon I'll whistle tunes
for everyone to hear.

I KNOW ALL THE SOUNDS
THAT THE ANIMALS MAKE

I know all the sounds that the animals make,
and make them all day from the moment I wake,
I roar like a mouse and I purr like a moose,
I hoot like a duck and I moo like a goose.

I squeak like a cat and I quack like a frog,
I oink like a bear and I honk like a hog,
I croak like a cow and I bark like a bee,
no wonder the animals
    marvel at me.

SOMERSAULTS

It's fun turning somersaults
and bouncing on the bed,
I walk on my hands
and I stand on my head.

I swing like a monkey
and I tumble and I shake,
I stretch and I bend,
but I never never break.

I wiggle like a worm
and I wriggle like an eel,
I hop like a rabbit
and I flop like a seal.

I leap like a frog
and I jump like a flea,
there must be rubber
inside of me.

HURRY GRANDMA HURRY

Hurry Grandma hurry,
Grandma look at me,
I'm right side up, I'm upside down,
I'm swinging from a tree.
I'm jumping like a squirrel,
I think that I can fly—
Grandma please don't worry,
Grandma please don't cry.

Hurry Grandma hurry,
see what I can do,
I'm roller-skating backwards
across the avenue.
Here's a luscious little bug,
I think I'll take a bite—
Grandma stop your screaming,
everything's all right.

Hurry Grandma hurry,
Grandma watch me please,
I'm climbing up a ladder,
I'm dangling by my knees.
I found this giant spider
that was stuck in gobs of paint,
Grandma take a closer look—
whatever made you faint?

My Brother Is a Quarterback

My brother is a quarterback,
I rarely catch a pass,
and he can run a marathon,
I soon run out of gas,
he pitches for his baseball team,
I pop up on his curve,
and he's an ace at tennis,
I can't return his serve.

My brother dunks the basketball,
I dribble like a mule,
he swims like a torpedo,
I flounder in the pool,
he's accurate at archery,
I hardly ever score,
he boxes and he wrestles,
I wind up on the floor.

My brother catches lots of fish,
I haven't any luck,
he's captain of his hockey team,
I can't control the puck,
his bowling's unbelievable,
I bowl like a buffoon,
he says someday I'll start to win…
I hope someday is soon.

LIFE'S NOT BEEN THE SAME IN MY FAMILY

Life's not been the same in my family
since the day that the new baby came,
my parents completely ignore me,
they scarcely remember my name.

The baby gets all their attention,
"Oh, isn't she precious!" they croon,
they think that she looks like an angel,
I think she resembles a prune.

They're thrilled when she giggles or gurgles,
"She burped!" they exclaim with delight,
they don't even mind when she wakes us
with deafening screams in the night.

They seem to believe she's a treasure,
there's simply no way I agree,
I wish she'd stop being a baby
and start being older than me.

My mother took me skating

My mother took me skating
and we glided on the ice,
I wasn't very good at it
and stumbled more than twice.

My mother made a figure eight,
and since it seemed like fun,
I tried a little trick myself
and made a figure one.

I HAVE A DOZEN DRAGONS

I have a dozen dragons,
I bought them at the mall,
I keep them in my closet,
It's fortunate they're small.
Their horns are red and silver,
Their scales are green and
    gold,
All of them are beautiful,
And all of them are bold.

They eat vanilla ice cream,
And pickles mixed with ink,
Then run around the kitchen
And jump into the sink.
They splash about the basin
And flap their silver wings,
While breathing tiny fires
That never burn a thing.

When we go out on weekends
And stroll around the block,
The neighbors stare in wonder,
They seem to be in shock.
I may not have a puppy,
A kitten, or a bird,
But I'm the only one I know
Who has a dragon herd.

MY CREATURE

I made a creature
out of clay,
just what it is
is hard to say.
Its neck is thin,
its legs are fat,
it's like a bear
and like a bat.

It's like a snake
and like a snail,
it has a little
curly tail,
a shaggy mane,
a droopy beard,
its ears are long,
its smile is weird.

It has four horns,
one beady eye,
two floppy wings
(though it can't fly),
it only sits
upon my shelf–
just think, I made it
by myself!

I SPIED MY SHADOW SLINKING

I spied my shadow slinking
up behind me in the night,
I issued it a challenge,
and we started in to fight.

I wrestled with that shadow,
but it wasn't any fun,
I tried my very hardest—
all the same, my shadow won.

I DON'T WANT TO

I don't want to play on the sidewalk.
I don't want to sit on the stoop.
I don't want to lick any ice cream.
I don't want to slurp any soup.
I don't want to listen to music.
I don't want to look at cartoons.
I don't want to read any stories.
I don't want to blow up balloons.

I don't want to dig in the garden.
I don't want to roll on the rug.
I don't want to wrestle the puppy.
I don't want to give you a hug.

I don't want to shoot any baskets.
I don't want to bang on my drum.
I don't want to line up my soldiers.
I don't want to whistle or hum.

I don't want to program my robot.
I don't want to strum my guitar.
I don't want to use my computer.
I don't want to wind up my car.
I don't want to color with crayons.
I don't want to model with clay.
I don't want to stop my not wanting . . .
I'm having that kind of a day.

TWADDLETALK TUCK

I'm Twaddletalk Tuck and I talk and I talk
and I talk when I run and I talk when I walk
and I talk when I hop and I talk when I creep
and I talk when I wake and I talk when I sleep
and I talk when it's wet and I talk when it's dry
and I talk when I laugh and I talk when I cry
and I talk when I jump and I talk when I land
and I talk when I sit and I talk when I stand
and I talk and I talk into anyone's ear
and I talk and I talk when there's nobody near
and I talk when I'm hoarse and my voice is a squawk
for I'm Twaddletalk Tuck and I talk and I talk.

THEY TELL ME I'M PECULIAR

They tell me I'm peculiar,
they seem to think I'm odd,
they look at me and grimace,
I smile at them and nod.

They cringe at my behavior,
"Unthinkable!" they say,
they're shocked that I love liver
and eat it every day.

I'M ALL MIXED UP

I'm AlL mixED uP,
i'M aLl MiXed Up,
I dON't KnoW whAT tO Do.
I dO NOt thINK i'M me tODAy,
i WoNdeR iF I'M YoU.
mY voICE is nOt My VOice TOday,
it sOUnDS enTIrELY wrONg,
and mANY ThOugHts iNsIDe mY hEaD
i'm CeRTaIN dON'T bEIOng.

My eYes aRE nOT My eYES toDaY,
mY nOse Is NOt MY nOSE,
my shOES aRE UNfAmiliaR,
I dOn'T REcOgnIZE mY cLOTheS.
My EaRs ArE NoT mY eArs tODay,
mY Hair iS nOt MY hAir,
I eVen thiNk i'M WeAriNg
soMeOnE elSe'S uNdERwEar.

NO mATter wHAt i wriTE ToDAy,
IT COMes oUt LOOking sTraNgE.
I HOpE ThaT i Can FIgurE ouT
a WaY TO maKE iT ChanGe.
i'M lOokinG cLOsELy at This pOEm,
bUT STilL dOn'T HAvE a CLue —
I'M ALL MIxED Up,
I'M alL MIxED uP,
i Don'T KNOw WHat To dO.

BE GLAD YOUR NOSE
IS ON YOUR FACE

Be glad your nose is on your face,
not pasted on some other place,
for if it were where it is not,
you might dislike your nose a lot.

Imagine if your precious nose
were sandwiched in between your toes,
that clearly would not be a treat,
for you'd be forced to smell your feet.

Your nose would be a source of dread
were it attached atop your head,
it soon would drive you to despair,
forever tickled by your hair.

Within your ear, your nose would be
an absolute catastrophe,
for when you were obliged to sneeze,
your brain would rattle from the breeze.

Your nose, instead, through thick and thin,
remains between your eyes and chin,
not pasted on some other place—
be glad your nose is on your face!

WHEN I AM FULL OF SILENCE

When I am full of silence,
and no one else is near,
the voice I keep inside of me
is all I want to hear.
I settle in my secret place,
contented and alone,
and think no other thoughts except
the thoughts that are my own.

When I am full of silence,
I do not care to play,
to run and jump and fuss about,
the way I do all day.
The pictures painted in my mind
are all I need to see
when I am full of silence . . .
when I am truly me.

I AM CUTER THAN A BUTTON

I am cuter than a button,
I am neater than a pin.
I have freckles on my forehead
and a dimple in my chin.

I have eyes as blue as bluebirds,
I have shiny golden hair,
and a little cherry birthmark—
I will never tell you where.

Tomorrow's My Unbirthday

Tomorrow's my unbirthday,
and I can hardly wait,
for every day I have one
is a day to celebrate.
I love unbirthday parties,
my friends enjoy them too,
we love to play unbirthday games . . .
I always win a few.

I love unbirthday presents,
they fill me with delight,
I love my grand unbirthday
    cakes
and savor every bite.
Tomorrow's my unbirthday,
I'm overjoyed, hooray!
I also had one yesterday,
I'm having one today.

A MILLION CANDLES

A million candles fill the night,
they glisten in the dark,
and though by day they hide their glow,
now each displays its spark.

Amidst them all, there is one light
that has a special shine,
and that's the one whose name I know...
I think that it knows mine.

I'M GLAD I'M ME

I'm glad I'm me, I'm glad I'm me,
There's no one else I want to be.
I'm happy I'm the person who
Can do the things that I can do.

If I were someone else, then I
Would feel so strange, I'd wonder why.
I'm positive that I'd be sad—
But I am me, and I am glad.